Developing Literacy Skills

Spelling

KEY STAGE 2: Y3-4/ P4-5

RAY BARKER
AND
GLEN FRANKLIN

HOPSCOTCH
EDUCATIONAL PUBLISHING

Contents

Published by Hopscotch Educational Publishing Company Ltd, Althorpe House, Althorpe Street, Leamington Spa CV31 2AU.

© 1998 Hopscotch Educational Publishing

Written by Ray Barker and Glen Franklin
Series design by Blade Communications
Illustrated by Susan Hutchison
Cover illustration by Pat Murray
Printed by Clintplan, Southam

Ray Barker and Glen Franklin hereby assert their moral right to be identified as the authors of this work in accordance with the Copyright, Designs and Patents Act, 1988.

ISBN 1-902239-07-5

Introduction

◆ ABOUT THE SERIES ◆

Developing Literacy Skills is a series of books aimed at developing key literacy skills using stories, non-fiction, poetry and rhyme, spelling and grammar, from Key Stage 1 (P1–3) through to Key Stage 2 (P4–7).

The series offers a structured approach which provides detailed lesson plans to teach specific literacy skills. A unique feature of the series is the provision of differentiated photocopiable activities aimed at considerably reducing teacher preparation time. Suggestions for using the photocopiable pages as a stimulus for further work in the classroom is provided to ensure maximum use of this resource.

◆ ABOUT THIS BOOK ◆

There is no one way to teach spelling. Good teachers use a variety of methods to give children a sense of pattern in language and the many exceptions to the rules that are found. What is clear is that structure and practice are both necessary. Children do not learn spelling skills through osmosis. The activities in this book develop through a phonological approach – but they are not slaves to phonics. The differentiated activities involve children in:
- investigating patterns and collecting examples of words
- reading and spelling words
- generating and practising new words

The activities are not meant to be followed in sequential order, and many of them are generic in that they can be developed and used in many different situations.

In English, spelling is a very difficult skill to learn. Rules can be taught and understood, but they only take children so far as the poem on page 64 illustrates so delightfully. Investigating sound patterns and playing with language through regular, concentrated and challenging practice can help them to understand the peculiarities of spelling.

◆ CHAPTER CONTENT ◆

◆ Overall aims

These outline the aims for both lessons.

◆ Teacher information

This provides background knowledge on the content of the lesson.

◆ Intended learning

This sets out the specific objectives for each lesson.

◆ Starting point

This provides ideas for introducing the activity.

◆ Activity

This explains the task(s) the children will carry out in the lesson without supporting photocopiable activities.

◆ Using the differentiated activity sheets

How to use each sheet and guidance on the type of child who will benefit most from each sheet.

◆ Plenary session

This suggests ideas for whole-class sessions to discuss the learning outcomes and follow-up work.

◆ Using the photocopiable sheets as a stimulus for further work

This is a useful list of further activities that can be developed from the activity sheets.

Other ideas for using . . .

This contains other ideas for developing the skill being addressed in this chapter.

Double consonants

Overall aims

- To look closely at words in order to investigate and collect words with double consonants.
- To read and spell words with double consonants.
- To generate and learn new words with double consonants.

Teacher information

- Children must sound out the words and hear the sounds they are making.
- Revise short and long vowel sounds.
- They must look closely at the words in these exercises in order to increase their visual awareness of when consonants are doubled – especially in the middle of words.
- If you are word-building on to **a single syllable word with a vowel before the last consonant, then the last letter will double** – *run: runner; swim: swimming*. This accounts for some of the spellings you may encounter – but not all!
- Listen to the vowel sound before the single or double letter. One rule might be: **double consonants in the middle of words come after a short vowel sound** – *apple: ape; puppy: pupil.*

LESSON ONE

Intended learning

- To investigate the rules for using double consonants.
- To write words with double consonants.

Starting point

- Use a fun approach, such as a tongue twister, to teaching this principle:

  Betty bought a bit of butter.
  Betty said: 'My butter's bitter.
  If I put it in my batter,
  It will make my batter bitter.
  Better buy some better butter.'

- Who can read it a line at a time? Which words cause the problems? Can anyone read it fast?
- What do they notice about many of the words that begin with *b*?
- Say the words and concentrate on the vowel sounds. What do they notice? (You may have to give them examples of long vowel sounds).
- Point out that double letters (both consonants) appear in the middle of words. This makes them more difficult to spell, as words such as *bet, bit, but* and *bat* do not end in the double letter.

Group activities

- More proficient children could collect words that contain double consonants from any source and write them on cards or small pieces of paper.
- They should pass these over to another group who could classify them on a large chart: words with double letters in the middle – *tummy*; words with double consonants at the end – *fall.*
- Another group could classify the words from the chart according to the letters used: *bb, dd, ff, ll, mm, nn, pp, rr, ss, tt.*
- Another group could examine the vowels before the double letter. Are they short or long?
- Children who find this concept difficult could copy and draw shape boxes around the words to increase visual awareness of this principle.
- Others could play sorting games using the word cards, such as *Snap* with *tt* words, or could collect sets of words using particular letters.

Plenary session

Bring the class together again to share ideas. How many different kinds of double consonant words are there? How many have *ss* at the end? How many have *bb* in the middle? Each group could report back and give their results. Are there any rules we can establish? Leave the charts and words on the Word Wall to provide the reference for the next session.

 LESSON TWO **Using the differentiated activity sheets**

 Intended learning

+ To read and spell words with double consonants.
+ To generate and learn new words with double consonants.

Starting point

+ Revise the work of the previous session by referring to the words on the wall and asking children to highlight the double consonants and their positions in a variety of words.
+ Revise what was learned about the position of the vowels before the double consonants and write any rules the children think are appropriate. These should be displayed and children given access to them when they are carrying out their activity sheets.
+ Locate dictionaries, thesauruses and any computer help available for their research.

Activity sheet 1

This provides children with simple picture activities in order that they can write and generate new words.

Activity sheet 2

This is aimed at those children who can collect, read and write new words using the shapes provided as a scaffolding.

Activity sheet 3

This is aimed at a higher level, and involves children working in pairs and generating words using the cube. They should be able to use reference sources to check their answers.

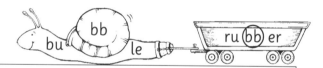

Plenary session

After each group has completed the activity, bring the whole class together to discuss their work.

For Activity sheet 1
What were the words illustrated by the pictures? What other words were generated? Are they spelled correctly? How do the children know? Does the spelling follow the rule which was discussed previously?

For Activity sheet 2
Ask the children to show their word snails and explain how they found and checked their words. Are they spelled correctly? Do they follow the rule?

For Activity sheet 3
Let some demonstrate the cube game to show how much they have learned.

Collect together all the words used and generated and write them on a Word Wall or put the separate sounds in separate columns. Summarise the rule.

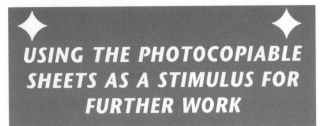

Double consonants

USING THE PHOTOCOPIABLE SHEETS AS A STIMULUS FOR FURTHER WORK

✦ Activity sheet 1

✦ Draw pictures of words written on the Word Wall to make cards. *Pelmanism* and *Snap* games can be played. If the word is written on the back, this can be read as a self-checking mechanism.
✦ Match pictures and words from the sheet.
✦ Draw shapes around the words (written in pencil). Rub out the pencil letters and ask children to write in the correct word according to shape and sound only.

✦ Activity sheet 2

✦ Cut up the snails and their examples and match the appropriate double letters.
✦ Blank out the double letters when the children have completed the sheet. Can they insert the correct ones from the clues of the other letters?
✦ Find examples of the letters appearing in other places in words, such as *ll* in *fell* and *yellow*.

✦ Activity sheet 3

✦ Collect all words made, print them on cards and play *Pelmanism* games with them.
✦ Use the new words in independent writing as much as possible by listing them first in independent word banks.
✦ Find out who can make the most words and which words do not really exist, such as *blugg*. What could this be if it did exist – an alien from a different planet?
✦ Encourage children to write and categorise their generated words.

Encourage the **Look, Say, Cover, Write, Say, Check** method for learning spellings.

OTHER IDEAS FOR DOUBLE CONSONANTS

✦ Give word searches containing words with double letters. This encourages visual awareness as they are looking for and circling the words.

✦ Puzzles can be made into a book and kept in the class library for all to use.

✦ Make books from the categorisations made so far on wall charts, such as double consonant words in alphabetical order; at the end or in the middle of words. Discuss the important features of information books with the children. What could make looking for words easier for other children in the class? For example, important parts of the words could be highlighted by colour – all *bb*s in red; making an index.

✦ Use the new double consonant words in independent writing. Encourage children to keep a *Try It* book in which they experiment with possible spellings. There should not be a stress on correctness at this stage but children should be critically working towards correctness.

✦ Encourage proofreading skills. If they discuss each other's work, they could learn something of professional proofreaders' marks and show when they think misspellings occur. Such marks could be researched and drawn by the children into a large class chart for all to see and use.

✦ Using IT is a way of seeing letters on screen – a talking word-processor is even better, as you can hear what you are writing and so can self-correct. If IT is used, children should compose straight onto screen. They should not write on paper and then copy on to the computer!

◆ Double consonants ◆

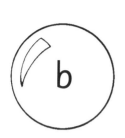

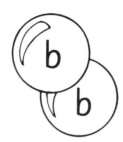

◆ Write the words under the pictures. Circle the double consonants.

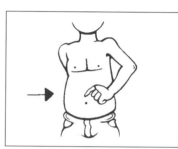

c l _ _ _   f _ _ _   t _ _ _ y

b _ _ _ _ e   r _ _ _ _ r   d _ _ _ _

◆ Can you find other words that use the same patterns?
Write them here.

_____   _____   _____

_____   _____   _____

_____   _____   _____

◆ Double consonants ◆

◆ Make a word using the letters on the snail's shell. Then write a different word on the trailer using the same two letters. The first one has been done for you.

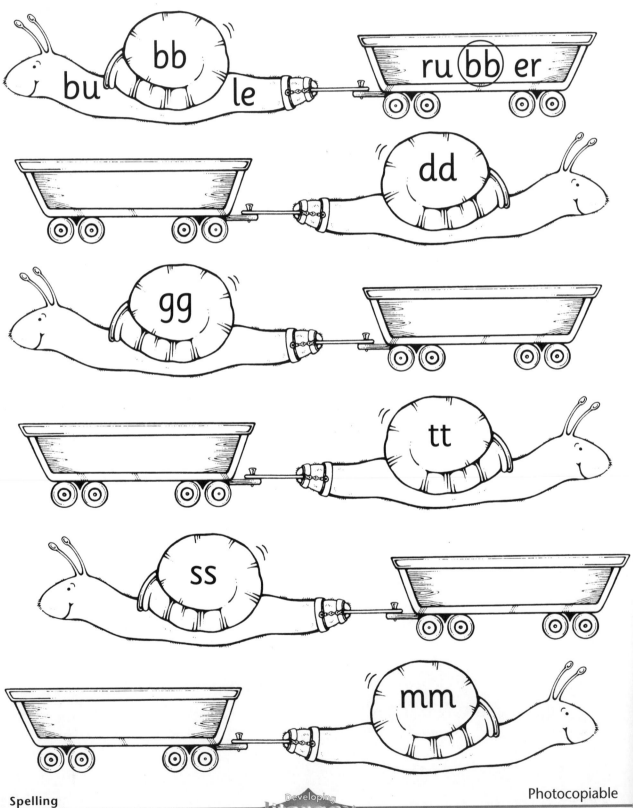

Developing literacy Skills

◆ Double consonants ◆

◆ Cut out and make these cubes. Challenge your partner to say,
write and spell words using the double consonant that is thrown.

ll

bb dd ff gg

mm

nn

tt dd rr pp

ss

Developing
Literacy
Skills

Common letter strings

Overall aims

- To investigate and collect words with common letter strings.
- To compare groups of words with common letters strings.
- To spell and learn groups of words with common letter strings.

Teacher information

- Children should sound out the words and hear the sounds they are making, but be aware that the written form may be different.
- They can be taught about letter strings from the earliest level. It is useful to link it to work on onset and rime as the same letter patterns in words such as *cat*, *hat*, *bat*, *mat* can then be reinforced.
- Give children experience of letter strings/patterns from written text. This is because English is sometimes an unreliable phonic language and what they hear and what is written and read may be different. For example, consider *read* and *bear*, *wood* and *food*.
- Visual awareness is all important. Children need to look for and find patterns, not just be told about them.

LESSON ONE

Intended learning

- To identify simple letter patterns.
- To generate words using patterns/letter strings and identify them in the new words.
- To write/practise words containing letter strings.

Starting point

- Ask the children to look for little words in big words in people's names in the class. Write a name on the board, such as *Ray*. Start by rhyming – *say*, *play*, *stay*. What do all these words have in common? Ask children to come to the front and circle the *ay* letter string. Now start to generate words from the string – payment. Summarise by pointing out to the children that if they can spell *Ray*, then they can use their knowledge to spell all the other words. Try this with some familiar letter strings, such as *ight* or *ough*. Ask the children to list words underneath. What patterns do they notice in the words? Circle them.

Group activities

- Give one group long words, or let them find long words in the dictionary. After considering their meaning they should look for small words in the long words – *knowledge* = *know*, *now*, *no*, *ledge* – and write them. Who can find the most ?
- Another group could take a series of children's names and find words in them – *Catherine* = *cat*, *the*, *her*, *in*. After they have written them they should answer the question: Which name provides the most words?
- Give another group more common letter strings, such as *our*, *are* and *ade*. Let them generate words and write them under the key word. Make it clear that the string can appear in any part of the word – not just at the end.
- They could pass the words to another group who could make them into cards to play *Snap* or other collecting and categorisation games.

Plenary session

Bring the class together again to share ideas. Groups finding words in long words should present their findings and announce the winner of the competition. Other children should write letter strings on the Word Wall and circle the patterns to show what they have learned. Finally, list all the letter strings dealt with in the session. Ask children to generate a simple word, for example if they can spell *our*, they can spell *your*, *four*, and *pour*. Leave the words on the wall as a reference for the next session.

LESSON TWO

 Using the differentiated activity sheets

 Intended learning

- ✦ To collect words with common letter strings.
- ✦ To compare groups of words with common letters strings.
- ✦ To spell and learn groups of words with common letters strings.

Activity sheet 1

This has been designed for children who need to identify simple letter strings. The cards can be used for a variety of games, but *Snap* and collecting words in one particular category are most useful.

Activity sheet 2

This aims to help children identify common letter strings and generate new words from them. These words should be more complicated with examples in all parts of the word – not only at the end or the beginning.

 Starting point

- ✦ Revise the work of Lesson 1 by generating words from a series of strings, such as all containing *a* – *are, ace, ate, ail*. Stress that they can be used in any part of the word. Remind the children that these letter patterns are found in many words, but they do not have to make the same sound. However, if they can spell one word containing the string (pattern) then there is no reason why they cannot spell all the words. Which words are nonsense? Which words are correct? How can they check?

Activity sheet 3

This is more difficult, in that it asks children to spell words containing common letter strings, identify patterns and word build.

 Plenary session

After each group has completed the activity, they should come together to discuss what they have been doing.

For Activity sheet 1
This group could explain the card game, read out all the words and put them into appropriate piles. The words could then be put onto the Word Wall or a wall chart in appropriate categories. Children should be asked to circle or mark in some ways the patterns that make the words common.

For Activity sheet 2
This group can explain the new words they have made with the satellites and what strings the words have in common.

For Activity sheet 3
This group should explain the concept of pyramids and what new words they discovered. Take an example from the pyramid sheet and model again how the words may get longer, the string may be in many places in the word, but it is there. Highlight the string to emphasise the pattern.

Common letter strings

USING THE PHOTOCOPIABLE SHEETS AS A STIMULUS FOR FURTHER WORK

◆ Activity sheet 1

To reinforce work on common letter strings, children could:
- ◆ cut up and match the beginning and endings of the words on the cards;
- ◆ use the cards in a wall display, for example collecting *ough* words. Children place the appropriate words around the letter string and join with a piece of cotton or string;
- ◆ test each other after choosing a card and investigating the meaning in a dictionary. For example, "I am thinking of the roof of a cottage made from straw. It begins with a *th*."

◆ Activity sheet 2

To generate and write more whole words containing common letter strings, children could:
- ◆ blank out the centre of the satellites and ask other children what is common to all the words surrounding it;
- ◆ challenging each other to find the words in dictionaries, give the meaning and spell them;
- ◆ re-categorise the words on the sheet by making a chart (according to letter string) and finding other examples with a partner.

◆ Activity sheet 3

- ◆ Give the pyramid lists to other children and ask them to circle the common letter strings.
- ◆ Cut up the strips of the pyramids and ask them to reassemble them, giving reasons, such as according to common letter string.
- ◆ Blank out all but the word at the base of the pyramid and ask children to work upwards, finding smaller words containing the letter string.

OTHER IDEAS FOR COMMON LETTER STRINGS

- ◆ Make word searches containing particular letter strings. Make them into a book for all the children to use. Use a program on a computer to make it look really professional.

- ◆ For those children really finding difficulty, concentrate on one string, such as *ing*. There are many rhymes for the word and it is also used as a suffix, for example end*ing*.

- ◆ Once a list of words has been assembled, such as *jingle*, *swing*, *doing* and *spring*, and the pattern has been isolated in all the words, children could investigate word building by playing spelling maths. One child should think about how one word can be used in order to build another and give his/her partner clues in mathematical terms: *swings – s + ing = swinging; single – le + s = sings.*

- ◆ Use the principle of building blocks. Divide words up into syllables or letter strings or onset and rime and see if the building blocks can be put together in interesting ways. How many new words can children find? How can they establish whether they are real words?

- ◆ Make class displays using the ideas of space satellites and pyramids so children have the words and the letter strings in front of them.

- ◆ Provide letter strings in handwriting practice so children can really focus on the visual patterns and on hand-eye co-ordination. Keep repeating the string, but ensure that the children always finish their lines of practice by writing an entire word using that string: *are, are, are, are, stare.*

✦ Common letter strings ✦

✦ Cut out these cards and use them to play games.

mail	night	thatch	our
tough	pail	right	although
match	hour	bone	fright
sail	favourite	rough	catch
attach	plough	nail	though
cough	phone	bright	stone
flight	railing	one	your

Name _____

✦ Common letter strings ✦

✦ Make new words from the letter strings.

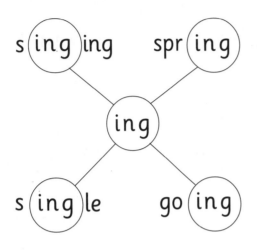

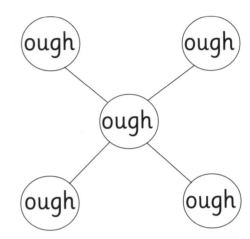

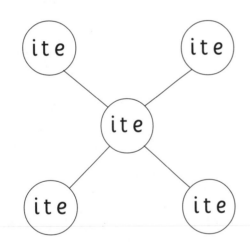

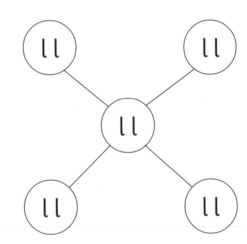

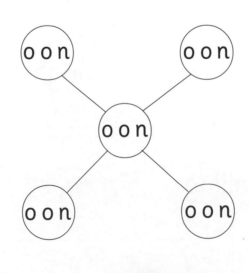

Developing literacy Skills

✦ Common letter strings ✦

✦ Build pyramids using the letter strings.
  Your words should get longer and longer!

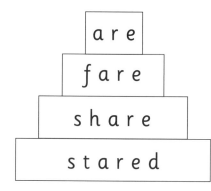

```
  a r e
 f a r e
s h a r e
s t a r e d
```

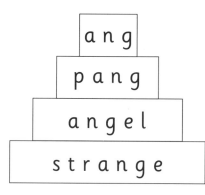

```
 a n g
p a n g
a n g e l
s t r a n g e
```

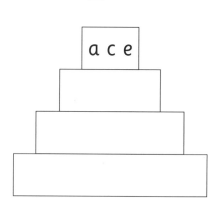

```
a c e
```

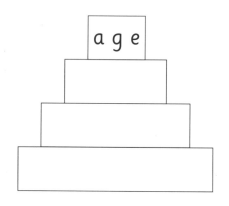

```
a g e
```

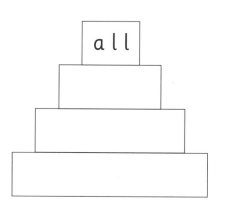

```
a l l
```

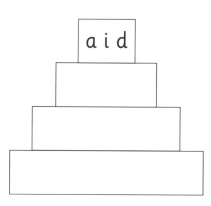

```
a i d
```

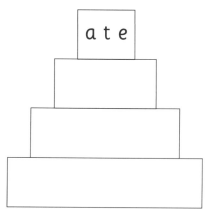

```
a t e
```

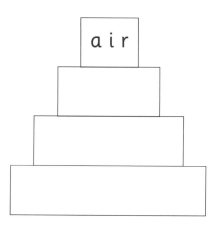

```
a i r
```

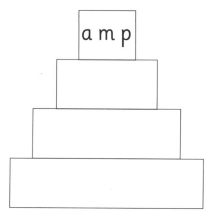

```
a m p
```

Spelling
KS2: Y3–4/P4–5

Developing
literacy
Skills

Photocopiable

15

Prefixes and suffixes

 ## Overall aims

+ To use the terms 'prefix' and 'suffix'.
+ To revise and extend list of known prefixes and suffixes.
+ To recognise and spell prefixes and suffixes.
+ To find and generate own words.
+ To understand how these parts influence word meaning.

 ## Teacher information

The most important issue concerning all these activities is that children should sound out the words and hear the sounds they are making. Prefixes and suffixes are always added to an existing root word. It is helpful to explain the origins of the words 'prefix' and 'suffix' as this will assist children's understanding of how they work. *Pre* means in *front of* or *before* – a prefix is always in front of the root word. 'Suffix' derives from a Latin word meaning *fastened below* – a suffix always follows on at the end of a root word.

 ## LESSON ONE

 ## Intended learning

+ To use the terms 'suffix' and 'prefix'.
+ To revise and extend list of known prefixes and suffixes.

Starting point

+ Provide some pictures that illustrate opposites – *happy/unhappy, tidy/untidy*. Ask the children to identify the words and write them on the board. Underline and name the prefix. Draw their attention to the fact that the root word remains the same. Explore how the prefix has changed the word meaning. Explain that the prefix *un* means *not*. Brainstorm and list other words starting with *un*, such as *unkind, unable*. Brainstorm and list

other known examples of prefixes. Using the root words *kind* and *happy,* add the suffix *ness* to the end of each. Discuss what has happened, emphasising the change in the root word, and introduce the term 'suffix'. Brainstorm and list known examples of suffixes.

 ## Group activities

Depending on the time allotted for the session, the groups could rotate around the activities. Explain that they will be looking for more examples of prefixes and suffixes, and exploring how they work.

+ Give some examples of prefixes and their origins, such as *bi* meaning *two, dis* meaning *not, ex* meaning *out of, re* meaning *again* or *back*. Ask them to explore in dictionaries and word banks to make a collection of words beginning with these prefixes and their meanings.
+ Give some examples of suffixes and their origins, such as *-ward* which shows direction, *-let* showing that something is small (piglet*), -ly* indicating how something is done (quietly*)*. Ask them to explore in dictionaries and word banks to make a collection of words beginning with these prefixes and record what they mean.
+ Give the children a variety of root words, prefixes and suffixes on cards. Ask them to make words and check them on a spell checker or word-processing program. This will begin to highlight exceptions and rules. Encourage the children to record their mistakes and identify the rules.

 ## Plenary session

Each group reports back on the activities and puts the work on a working wall display. Add new examples of prefixes and suffixes to the class lists. As a closing activity play *In the Manner of the Word*. Ask the children to mime an activity, such as "Alev, walk to the door noisily", "Tony, feed the hamster quietly."

 LESSON TWO

✦ Intended learning

- ✦ To recognise and spell prefixes and suffixes.
- ✦ To find and generate own words.
- ✦ To understand how these parts influence word meanings.

✦ Starting point

- ✦ Revise the work from the previous lesson, reminding the children what they discovered about prefixes and suffixes. Put a selection of words on the white board or easel and ask the children to identify and name the parts of the words. Remind the class of the origin of word meanings of prefix and suffix.

✦ Using the differentiated activity sheets

It is important to stress the use of dictionaries or spell checkers throughout to ensure that spelling rules and their exceptions are identified.

Activity sheet 1

This is for children who need further reinforcement of the concept of prefixes and suffixes, and to be able to spell some simple examples.

Activity sheet 2

This is for children who are ready to widen their experience. The activity focuses on using suffixes, allowing them to explore spelling rules and generate their own new words.

Activity sheet 3

This is aimed at children who need to extend their experience through generating their own words, spelling these and investigating word meaning and vocabulary.

✦ Plenary session

For Activity sheet 1
Using magnetic letters on a whiteboard, make a root word, such as *like* and ask "Can you add a prefix to this word to make it say the opposite?" There could be a variety of answers – *unlike*, *dislike*. Use a root word, such as *play*. Ask "Can you add a suffix to change this word's meaning?" Accept any of the alternatives – *playing*, *player*, *played* and ask for a sentence using it.

For Activity sheet 2
Enlarge the rules and read them aloud. Ask for an example of this rule in action. Prompt for examples that prove/disprove the rule.

For Activity sheet 3
As above, but also prompt for identification of whether prefixes, suffixes or both were used, word meanings and other rules that they may have found.

Finally, play a game. Start the children off with a root word, such as *play*. In turns around the class, each child has to link to the word, either giving another version of the root word, or using the same prefix or suffix. Play might continue like this: *play, playing, singing, liking, liked, disliked, disappear, appear, reappear . . .* and so on.

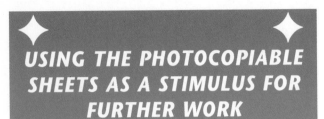
Prefixes and suffixes

USING THE PHOTOCOPIABLE SHEETS AS A STIMULUS FOR FURTHER WORK

◆ Activity sheet 1

- ✦ Collect examples of prefixes and suffixes and build up a word bank. Practise spelling them using **Look, Say, Cover, Write, Say, Check**.
- ✦ Develop the *Prefix and Suffix Trail*, and display this around the classroom.
- ✦ Make flip books to experiment with generating known and new words.

◆ Activity sheet 2

- ✦ Give each group an example of the rules relating to suffixes. They collect words that illustrate the rule and make a rule book. This can become a classroom resource which may be added to.
- ✦ Sort and classify words with prefixes and suffixes. Discuss with a partner reasons for sorting. Find a way to record the work – a Venn or Tree diagram.
- ✦ Explore the crossword facilitity of a spellchecker or portable computer. Type in a root word, with two or three question marks before or after the word. Record the options given. Do all the words generated have suffixes and prefixes? Record the words and find out their meaning.

◆ Activity sheet 3

- ✦ Design a cloze procedure exercise, in story form, giving the root word but omitting the prefix or suffix.
- ✦ Collect and explore word families, looking at root words that can be extended in different ways – *music, musician, musical, unmusical, musically*. Note and record the spelling conventions.
- ✦ Draw a character from a known text. Find words to describe the character which use prefixes or suffixes – *unkind, helpful, telepathic*.

OTHER IDEAS FOR PREFIXES AND SUFFIXES

- ✦ Score a word! How many points can you score by adding a prefix or suffix to a root word, such as *take, mistake, mistaken, mistakenly*, scores 3 points. Have a class challenge! You could make the scoring more complicated if you have a particularly competitive class, for example double the points if two suffixes are added. Perhaps points will need to be deducted for the wrong spelling rule applied.

- ✦ Explore prefix antonyms. Find pairs of words that are opposite in meaning but both have a prefix – *side: inside/outside; arm: overarm/underarm*.

- ✦ Explore different ways of sorting and classifying words, for example by the origin of the prefix, Greek or Latin perhaps, or words where the same rule applies.

- ✦ Keep in mind that there is a real relationship between handwriting and spelling. Writing letter strings in a consistent and regular way helps children to register patterns in a multi-sensory way.

- ✦ Continue to draw attention to examples of prefixes and suffixes during shared reading and writing sessions, and add constantly to the words banks and collections.

◆ Prefixes and suffixes ◆

✦ Catch the right fish to change the words to their opposite meanings.

✦ Now write each of the words you have made in the correct sentence.

That is an _____ answer.

You will find books about insects in a _____ book.

I like carrots but I really _____ cabbage.

Don't be _____ to your baby brother.

✦ Add some suffixes.

	ed	ing	er
play			
talk			
jump			
help			

✦ Which of the words go in the sentences?

The children _____ loudly in the playground.

The frog went _____ back to its pond.

Jane is a brilliant football _____ .

Dad is _____ me with my homework tonight.

✦ Suffix rules! ✦

✦ Does the root word end in a single consonant and have a short vowel?

✦ Does the suffix begin with a vowel (including *y*)?

DOUBLE THE CONSONANT!

✦ Does the root word end in a silent *e*?

✦ Does the suffix begin with a vowel?

DROP THE *E*!

✦ Does the root word end in a consonant followed by a *y*?

CHANGE THE *Y* TO AN *I* BEFORE ADDING ALL SUFFIXES EXCEPT *ING*!

LET'S INVESTIGATE!

✦ Here are some root words.

lucky	happy	play
take	like	rain
help	colour	kind

✦ Here are some suffixes.

ing	ly	er
ful	ed	ness

✦ On a separate piece of paper see how many words you can make. Check your spelling using a dictionary or spell checker.

How many words did you find?

Developing literacy Skills

Photocopiable

◆ What can it mean? ◆

◆ Here is a mixture of root words, suffixes and prefixes.

happy
play
kind
rest
view

in
un
dis
inter
re

ful
ness
ly
ing
ed

◆ Find as many words as you can, using a dictionary or spellchecker to help you.

◆ Think what each word means.

◆ Which spelling rule did you use?

root word	my word	means . . .	spelling rule . . .

◆ Challenge your friend – who can find the most words?

Overall aims

✦ To investigate and collect words using silent letters.
✦ To spell and read words incorporating silent letters.
✦ To formulate and use rules that apply to words with silent letters and note any exceptions.

 Teacher information

There are historical reasons for many words having silent letters – *k* as in *knight* used to be pronounced, but laziness accounts for its being dropped. An Old English letter, no longer existing, used to make the *wh* sound. When printers came to represent the sound they used this letter combination. Many of the peculiarities can be put down to issues when transferring from an oral culture to a print culture. When books were first printed, printers used to insert a *b* in words to make them sound more Latinate! The silent *e* may cause problems. A rule may be 'Listen to words that have a silent *e*. The earlier vowel says its name and not its sound – *hat*: *hate*.' Children will benefit from knowing the difference between vowels and consonants and the long and short sounds that vowels can make.

 **◆ LESSON ONE ◆**

 Intended learning

✦ To investigate and collect words with silent letters.
✦ To read and spell words containing a variety of silent letters.
✦ To move towards formulating some spelling rules about selected silent letters.

 Starting point

✦ Start with *b*, using a rhyme – Mary had a little lamb. Ask the children to say *lamb* out loud, then take the word letter by letter and say the individual sounds. What do they notice about the *b*? Point out that this is called a silent letter and

there are many examples in English. Can they think of any more words using a silent *b*? You could mime some – *bomb, comb, thumb, crumb, climb, tomb*. Ask them to write them on the board. Do the same using *k – knight, knife, knee, knot.* This time the silent letter is at the beginning. Explain that up to about 1500, people pronounced the letters. Have fun doing this to get them used to the letters in the words. Look at all the words on the board. Look at the letters before and after the silent letters. Are there any patterns? (An *n* after a silent *k* and an *m* before a silent *b*.)

 Group activities

✦ Start with the same letters. Can children add to the list through their own research?
✦ Using letters of the alphabet, find words in which the letters are sounded and words in which the letters are silent, such as *h* in *house* and *rhyme*; *g* as in *gun* and in *gnome*.
✦ Look at the *t* in *winter* and *castle*. When they have grasped the principle from one word then they should be able to generate more by analogy or research them – *castle, whistle, rustle, listen.*
✦ Write silly sentences using the same silent letter – *The knight with a knife is on his knees.*
✦ To illustrate the silent *e* principle, give children endings, such as *ace, age, ade*, and ask them to word build and generate words. Ask them to circle the ends of the words to discover any principle.

 Plenary session

How many silent letters have they found? List words on a Word Wall. Ask children to read words how they are pronounced and how they are spelled to notice the difference between them. Silly sentences could be shared and read. Finally, see if any rules can be established and write them up (you may have to prompt), such as silent *e* and the previous vowel sound, *g* always before an *n*, *r* and *h* going together and *s* before *t*.

 LESSON TWO

Intended learning

+ To identify and categorise words with silent letters.
+ To write words containing a variety of silent letters, after research.
+ To formulate some spelling rules about selected silent letters.

Starting point

+ Revise the work of the previous session, including what was learned about the position of the silent letters and write any rules the children think are appropriate. Children should have access to them when they are carrying out their activities. Orally generate some examples and ask children to spell the words according the rules they have identified. Point out the location of dictionaries, thesauruses and any computer help available for their research.

Using the differentiated activity sheets

Activity sheet 1

This has been designed for children who need to read the words and identify the silent letters. They should be able to categorise these words in a simple way.

Activity sheet 2

This is aimed at children who can read the words on the Word Wall and in books, who can sound them out and who can use information and research skills to help generate further examples.

Activity sheet 3

This is aimed at those children who can link clues to examples and generate new words. Point out that some of the clues may apply to more than one word.

Plenary session

Bring the class together to discuss what they have been doing and what they have discovered or learned.

For Activity sheet 1
This group could list all the words on their sheet with silent letters and explain why the remaining words are not examples of these. How did they categorise them. Can the others find other words to put in these categories?

For Activity sheet 2
These children could list all the new words they have generated, but explain how they illustrate the principle of silent letters.

For Activity sheet 3
This group should outline the clues they have been discussing and provide examples. Are any of these new to the class? Can others find new examples?

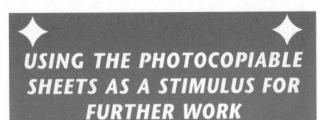

Silent letters

USING THE PHOTOCOPIABLE SHEETS AS A STIMULUS FOR FURTHER WORK

✦ Activity sheet 1

✦ Isolate one kind of silent letter only, such as the silent *e* and concentrate on that using common examples.

✦ Cut out the words and ask others to stack them in relevant piles, such as according to letter and according to position of silent letter.

✦ Blank out some of the silent letters and ask others to replace them.

✦ Trace over the words using a coloured pencil, saying each letter that they write.

✦ Activity sheet 2

✦ Cut up the strips to the left and the right and match them.

✦ Use only the examples on the right and ask children to identify the silent letters after reading them.

✦ Practise dictionary skills further by giving each other one of the word-beginning sounds and asking how many words with silent letters they can collect in a set amount of time.

✦ Activity sheet 3

✦ Give others just a rule cut from the sheet and ask them to find a number of words from sources around the room to illustrate the rule.

✦ Use the examples on the sheet to test others but use the definition only (looked up in a dictionary) to test others' knowledge, such as "I'm thinking of a small garden object holding a fishing rod. It's second letter is a *n*."

✦ Blank out the examples and ask others to find a word linked to the rule and to a certain letter of the alphabet. Ask someone else to check answers in the dictionary.

OTHER IDEAS FOR SILENT LETTERS

✦ Find examples of other rhymes using silent letters, such as *Old Mother Hubbard* and her cupboard, *Little Jack Horner* and his thumb, *Little Miss Muffet* and her whey. In this way, the children will be thoroughly reading and investigating the rhymes to identify words.

✦ Read around the room to find other silent letters in well-known words – *February* and *Wednesday*. Find out why this should be. This is a useful introduction to word derivation and the idea that English is a mixture of languages from many cultures, in this case *February* is from Latin, a heritage of the Roman occupation; *Wednesday* from Wodensday – a part of our Viking heritage.

✦ Some animals have silent letters in their names, such as a *gnu* and a *rhinoceros*. Creative writing could be centred upon alliterative ideas, such as *A gnome and a gnu gnawed a gnat!*

✦ Some children could use the many words illustrated around the class to make word searches for others in the class, for example a *k* word search might be in the shape of a castle and have a knightly medieval theme for display.

✦ On a class display, write the various rules out large surrounded by a selection of words on cards. Provide children with the opportunity to join words to the rules with string.

✦ For a more kinetic display, make large letters (that appear as silent in words) and cut them out. Hang words containing that silent letter from them. Ask children to design the mobiles, paying careful attention to the principles of balance necessary. In this way the words will act as reference right above their heads.

✦ Silent letters ✦

✦ Look at the words below. Which have silent letters? Put a tick or a cross. Then circle the letters that you do not pronounce.

(g)nat   ✔   wash ☐   hour ☐   whole ☐

lamb ☐   write ☐   snake ☐   hat ☐

listen ☐   talk ☐   island ☐   hole ☐

psalm ☐   farm ☐   autumn ☐   knee ☐

rabbit ☐   crumb ☐   wriggle ☐   rhyme ☐

✦ Now sort the words into these boxes.

Silent at the beginning	Silent in the middle	Silent at the end
gnat		

Silent letters

◆ Spell, read and write words with silent letters.

Shhh...

At the beginning of words

		New examples
qu	queen quiz	
kn	knee	
gn	gnat	
rh	rhyme	
wr	wrestle	
ch	chemist	

At the end of words

		New examples
_ mb	thumb	
_ gh	rough	
_ mn	autumn	
_ tle	whistle	

Developing
literacy
Skills

✦ Silent letters ✦

✦ Join the clues to the example and then to the silent letter or letters. There may be more than one example for each clue.

Clues	Examples	Silent letters

Clues

This silent letter comes after **m**.

This silent letter comes before **t**.

This silent letter usually makes the previous vowel long.

This silent letter comes before **n**.

These silent letters come before **t**.

This silent letter comes before **r**.

This silent letter is at the beginning.

This silent letter comes after **r**.

This silent letter comes after **w**.

This silent letter comes after **s**.

Examples

whip

bomb

rhinoceros

debt

honest

hate

gnome

bright

knife

castle

wrestle

Silent letters

g

gh

e

b

k

h

t

w

Developing literacy Skills

Plural nouns

 Overall aims

- To investigate, collect and classify spelling patterns for the pluralisation of nouns.
- To spell and read plural nouns.
- To identify and learn basic rules for plural nouns.
- To generate new words according to the rules and note exceptions.

 Teacher information

Children need to be fully conversant with what a noun is and to know that most plural nouns have an extra *s*. General exceptions to these are nouns:

- ending in *s, sh, tch, x* and *z*, or with a *ch* sounding like *tch* (church) use *es* in the plural form.
- ending in *o* use *es* in the plural form (potatoes) unless ending in two vowels (kangaroos, patios).
- ending with a consonant and a *y* change the *y* to an *i* and add *es* in the plural form (babies, teddies).
- ending in *f* or *fe* sometimes change the *f* to a *v* and add *es* (shelves), but not always (beliefs).

There are many exceptions to these rules, known as 'Irregular Plural Forms'. Children will encounter these and you should draw attention to them when they occur. Encourage the use of dictionaries and spell checks before the word is committed to memory.

more than one, the word needs to change a bit more than just adding an *s*. Ask if they can think of any examples. Show them an object or a picture, such as a baby. Write the word on the board and ask them to read it aloud. Now bring in more than one. Ask them to predict what to write. Scribe the correct spelling and draw the children's attention to the changes in the word.

 Group activities

Each group should explore a particular plurals spelling rule, using dictionaries or word banks, which can be shared with the whole class in the Plenary session. Provide nouns written on cards and ask the children to find out how they are spelled in the plural form. They should say what is happening and record and classify findings. They then should look for new nouns that fit with their classification.

- One group should use nouns that end in *y* (boy, party).
- One group should use nouns that end in vowels (potatoes, radios). Beware of irregular words, such as piano, at this stage.
- One group should use nouns that end in *f* (beliefs, wolves).

 **LESSON ONE**

 Intended learning

- To investigate, collect and classify spelling patterns for pluralisation of nouns.
- To spell and read plural nouns.

 Starting point

- Remind the children what they know already about adding extra *s* and check their understanding by prompting some of them to write given words on the board, or to generate their own. Explain that sometimes, when there is

 Plenary session

Each group should report back on the activities, explain their findings and give the class an opportunity to put them to the test. Display the findings for future reference.

As a closing activity, to give further opportunity to spell the words, give each child a noun, differentiated to ability, and ask them to write the plural word on the board, explaining which spelling rule, if any, they were using.

◆ LESSON TWO ◆

◆ Intended learning

✦ To identify and learn basic rules for plural nouns.
✦ To generate new words according to the rules and note exceptions.

◆ Starting point

✦ Revise the work from the previous lesson. Remind the children what they discovered about changing nouns from singular to plural. Ask them to reiterate some of the discoveries they made, referring to their classifications and findings.

◆ Using the differentiated activity sheets

Explain to the children that they are now going to explore the rules that help to make spelling plural nouns easier. Explain that not all nouns follow the rules and that they may come across some of these in their work. Indeed, they may have already found some! Ask the children to keep a note of any of these irregular noun plurals they come across. You will be using them in some work later on.

Activity sheet 1

This is aimed at children who need reinforcement of spelling and reading the basic plural forms of *s* and *es*.

Activity sheet 2

This is aimed at children who have grasped the basic plural forms and are ready to explore further and learn the rules.

Activity sheet 3

This is aimed at children who have consolidated their knowledge of the basic plural form and are able to apply this into generating, reading and spelling words of their own.

◆ Plenary session

Bring the whole class together to share and discuss the work. Use this time to assess the understanding of each group, by prompting questions.

For Activity sheet 1
Provide a mixture of nouns, some that have a single *s* for the plural and some *es*. Choose a card at random. Ask someone to read it then write the plural on the board. Encourage the child to explain reasons for choice.

For Activity sheet 2
The children will have identified four different spelling rules. Using their results, they explain what they found out, giving the rules in their own words. Ask each child to generate a new word that corresponds to the rule.

For Activity sheet 3
As above. Encourage the children to read their new words aloud. Put out some other words on the board or on cards. Ask the children to place these in the catagories they have designed.

As a concluding activity, use a shared writing session to agree a class statement of spelling rules for regular noun pronouns. Produce this as a working wall display so that children may add to it as new words are found or generated. Provide space for exceptions to the rules. Encourage children to record these, and discuss them during class sessions.

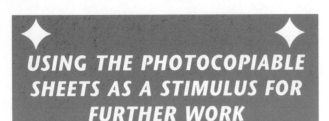

Plural nouns

USING THE PHOTOCOPIABLE SHEETS AS A STIMULUS FOR FURTHER WORK

◆ Activity sheet 1

To consolidate their work on plural nouns using *s* or *es* endings, the children could:
◆ plan other activities, such as equipment for a cooking lesson. They will encounter plural spellings other than *s* and *es*. Encourage the use of dictionaries;
◆ play *Plurals Bingo*. Mount regular singular nouns on card. Put a mixture of *s* and *es* endings on A4 baseboards. Take turns to turn over a card, read the word then match it to the correct ending on the baseboard. Use dictionaries for adjudication.

◆ Activity sheet 2

To consolidate their work on spelling rules for plural nouns, the children could:
◆ design a spelling rule book;
◆ play *Rules Pairs* or *Happy Families*. Provide a collection of words. They collect pairs or sets that reflect the same group of spelling conventions;
◆ collect examples of plurals from known story texts. Extracts could be used to experiment with cloze procedure – changing plural to singular.

◆ Activity sheet 3

To consolidate work on generating words through applying spelling rules, the children could:
◆ sort and classify according to given attributes, reading and recording their own words;
◆ make sorting games for others, using their own collection of words and following the given rules;
◆ collect and explore word families and note the similarities – do words that have come into English from other languages exhibit similar behaviour? Do words in catagories, for example 'food', conform to the same rules?

OTHER IDEAS FOR PLURAL NOUNS

◆ Exceptions to the rules! These will have been occuring all the time. A 'by the way . . . ' type of recording system in the class should by now have given some good examples – *mouse, mice, tooth, teeth, child, children, sheep, sheep.*

◆ Continue to investigate and record these in shared reading and writing activities. It is particularly important to support children who may speak English as an additional language. For example, some Indian languages do not have a aural distinction between singular and plural. Over-application of the rules can result in *sheeps, mens,* and so on.

◆ Examine patterns in irregular plurals – *men, women, geese, teeth,* and at the exceptions to the exceptions – *mouse, mice,* but not *house, hice*! And what is the plural for a computer mouse?

◆ It is probably safe to asume that the majority of words will fall into the regular plural nouns catagory and will fit in with the rules examined in the activity sheets. However it will support the children if the irregular forms are available as a reference in the classroom, to avoid over-generalising of the spelling rules.

Generally, encourage the children to use the **Look, Say, Cover, Write, Say, Check** method for learning spellings, and to refer to dictionary and other sources to ensure that their own generated words are correct.

Keep in mind that there is a real relationship between handwriting and spelling. Writing letter strings in a consistent and regular way helps children to register patterns in a multi-sensory way.

Name _____

A party!

✦ You are having a party. Six people are coming. Make sure you have six of everything you need.

REMEMBER
Words ending with **ss**, **x**, **ch** or **sh** need to use **es** if there are more than one.

cake

pie

box

plate

dish

drink

glass

sausage

peach

✦ What else might you need? Make a list, then use a dictionary to spell the plural words.

I need	
one	**six**

Spelling

KS2: Y3–4/P4–5

Developing
Literacy
Skills

Photocopiable

31

◆ What's the rule? ◆

✦ Look at the words in the boxes. Use a dictionary to
   check how to spell them in plural form.

lady	tomato	leaf	boy

_____ _____ _____ _____

shelf	puppy	hero	key

_____ _____ _____ _____

birthday	toy	wolf	baby

_____ _____ _____ _____

city	half	echo	potato

_____ _____ _____ _____

✦ Now sort the plural words into these boxes.

_____ _____ _____ _____ **What's the rule?**	_____ _____ _____ _____ **What's the rule?**
_____ _____ _____ _____ **What's the rule?**	_____ _____ _____ _____ **What's the rule?**

✦ Spelling plural nouns ✦

✦ Look at these nouns. Use a dictionary to help you spell the plural form.

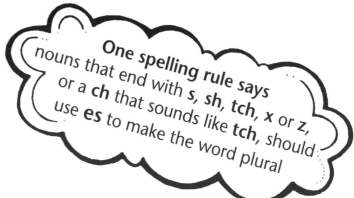

One spelling rule says nouns that end with **s**, **sh**, **tch**, **x** or **z**, or a **ch** that sounds like **tch**, should use **es** to make the word plural

glass	baby
_____	_____
box	loaf
_____	_____
hero	teddy
_____	_____
fish	scarf
_____	_____
potato	lunch
_____	_____

✦ Which words agree with the rule above?

_____

_____

_____

_____

✦ Sort the remaining words into these three boxes. What is the rule for each of these? Find some more of your own for each box.

the rule is	the rule is	the rule is
_____	_____	_____
_____	_____	_____

Spelling

KS2: Y3–4/P4–5

Developing
literacy
Skills

Photocopiable

33

Overall aims

+ To spell regular two-syllable words by building words from known parts.
+ To spell syllables from phonemic parts.
+ To collect and explore examples of short words within longer words.
+ To collect, compare and generate compound words and words with common parts.
+ To identify syllabic beats in polysyllabic words, using the term syllable appropriately.
+ To investigate, practise and learn spellings of regular polysyllabic words.

 Teacher information

By this age, children will have explored rhythm. They will have identified the number of syllables in a word and named the parts. This ability to hear and recognise the parts of the words provides a secure basis for children to explore, generate and spell words, building from known parts into new words. The most important issue concerning all these activities is that children should sound out the words and hear the sound they are making. Teachers must ensure that the children are familiar with the term 'syllable' and are using it appropriately.

 LESSON ONE

 Intended learning

+ To spell regular two syllable words by building words from known parts.
+ To spell syllables from phonemic parts.

Starting point

+ Begin by reinforcing the concept of a syllable as a part, or beat, of a word, using the children's names, familiar rhymes and class word collections. Check that the children understand and use the term 'syllable' correctly. Then, take a familiar monosyllabic word, such as *for*.

Brainstorm and list words that include this word *forget, forest, fortune*. The children could also identify words such as *before* and *therefore*, which have the same sound. Explore and discuss this with them.

 Group activities

+ *Syllable Jigsaw.* Using photographs or collections of objects, such as 'things we eat', mount the name of each object on card and cut them up into syllabic parts – *ap/ple, but/ter, co/co/nut*. Ask the children to remake the words and match them to the pictures, then write the words and record their work for display.
+ Using dictionaries and word banks give the group a known word, such as *cat* and ask them to collect examples of this word in longer words (*catapult, caterpillar*).
+ Provide a syllabic part of a word, such as *mit*, and ask them to use dictionaries and word banks to collect examples of this word in longer words (*limit, admit, mittens*).

In both the latter two activities, the crossword facility on a spellchecker could be used. The children write, read and learn their words, using **Look, Say, Cover, Write, Say, Check.**

 Plenary session

Bring the whole class together for a plenary session. Each group should report back on the activities and put the work on a working wall display.

As a closing activity, play *Syllable Hangman.* Choose a word from the class collection. The children have to identify the parts of the word rather than the individual letters, for example *pea/nut/but/ter*. Give clues at first if necessary.

◆ LESSON TWO ◆

◆ Intended learning

- ◆ To collect and explore examples of short words within longer words.
- ◆ To collect, compare and generate compound words and words with common parts.
- ◆ To identify syllabic beats in polysyllabic words, using the term syllable appropriately.

◆ Starting point

- ◆ Remind the children what they discovered about syllables and parts of words. Introduce the concept of compound words. Write a known word, such as *play*, on the board. Brainstorm and list associated words, such as *playground, playtime, playdough*. Examine each part of the word and what it means. Identify and name the syllables. Introduce the term 'compound words'. Investigate and explore other compound words and words with common parts, such as *underground, postcard, overtake, airport*.

◆ Using the differentiated activity sheets

Explain to the children that they will be investigating more compound words with common parts. Emphasise the need to identify and record the syllables of the words they collect.

Activity sheet 1

This is aimed at children who have built up a small sight vocabulary, but are experiencing difficulty generating by analogy. They may still be unsure when attempting to hear and identify syllables.

Activity sheet 2

This is aimed at children who can recognise and spell a variety of known words, can generate from known to unknown words and are confidently identifying regular two syllable words.

Activity sheet 3

This is aimed at children who are able to make up compound words using a given link word. You might want to point out that the link word might be used at the beginning or end of the compound word.

◆ Plenary session

After the children have completed their tasks, bring the whole class together to share and discuss the work. This time can be used to assess the understanding of each group, by prompting questions using the whiteboard and a collection of parts of compound words as used on the sheets.

For Activity sheet 1
Display a selection of words from the activity sheet. Ask a child, "Please make a word using two of these cards". Prompt the child to read the word and identify the number of syllables.

For Activity sheet 2
Ask the child to choose one of the shopping baskets from the activity sheet and read the words aloud. Ask, "What new word did you find? How many syllables does your new word have? Which of your baskets had the most syllables?"

For Activity sheet 3
Ask the child what each ship was named. Discuss any difficulties, such as did the child use *nowhere, everywhere* and *somewhere*, or *nothing, everything* and *something*? Which ship used the word *any*? This could have been used in conjunction with *thing* or *way*!

As a closing activity, play *Compound Word Links*. Begin with a word, such as *play*. The children in turn provide the link words – *playground, underground, underarm, overarm, overtake*, and so on.

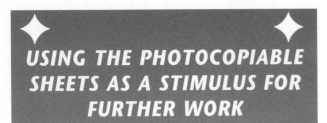

Syllables and word building

USING THE PHOTOCOPIABLE SHEETS AS A STIMULUS FOR FURTHER WORK

✦ Activity sheet 1

To consolidate work on building from simple known words and identifying syllables, the children could:
✦ collect and categorise words, such as names of animals, according to the number of syllables; Explore words within words – *pot* in *hippopotamus*;
✦ read, write and learn the parts from common compound words – *play, over, where* – and make collections of these for class reference;
✦ read, write and learn the parts from regular two-syllable words – *let/ter* – and apply the parts to generate new words.

✦ Activity sheet 2

To consolidate their work on recognising, generating and spelling regular compound words and words with common parts, the children could:
✦ make flip books of collections of compound words, illustrating each word separately;
✦ explore definitions of each part of the word, categorising the results;
✦ develop the shopping trolley activity by giving the children a collection of word parts and a specified number of syllables to 'spend'.

✦ Activity sheet 3

To consolidate their work on sorting, classifying and generating compound words according to their own criteria, the children could:
✦ explore the use of prefixes and suffixes to extend the syllable cargo of each of their ships;
✦ design a word-building treasure hunt for other children to play;
✦ explore words that are used in a variety of compounds – *anywhere, anyhow, anyway, anything*. Can the class find the word with the most uses?

OTHER IDEAS FOR SYLLABLES AND WORD BUILDING

✦ What is a syllable? Academics are still debating the definitive definition! However, it would be useful for the children to explore the fact that every syllable must have at least one vowel. For this explanation the letter *y* becomes an honorary vowel.

✦ Explore polysyllabic words using this rule. See if they can find an exception.

✦ Encourage the children to look for chunks of words they know and to apply these when learning and spelling new words, for example *suddenly, fantastic*.

Generally, encourage the children to use the **Look, Say, Cover, Write, Say, Check** method for learning spellings.

Keep in mind that there is a real relationship between handwriting and spelling. Writing letter strings in a consistent and regular way helps children to register patterns in a multi-sensory way.

Activity 1

Name _____

◆ Little words in bigger ones ◆

◆ Match each beginning word with a group of letters from this box. Use a dictionary to help you.

toon	erpillar	alogue	penter
nap	dy	not	dle	pet

word	how many syllables?

cat

word	how many syllables?

car

word	how many syllables?

can

◆Shopping for compound words◆

✦ Choose words from the shelves to fill the baskets. Then use a dictionary find another word for each basket. Add up the number of syllables each basket holds.

✦ Syllable Island ✦

✦ There are lots of words buried on the island. Each ship needs to collect three words. Gather three words to go with each link word that is written on the ship. Write them on the sails. How many syllables does each ship carry?

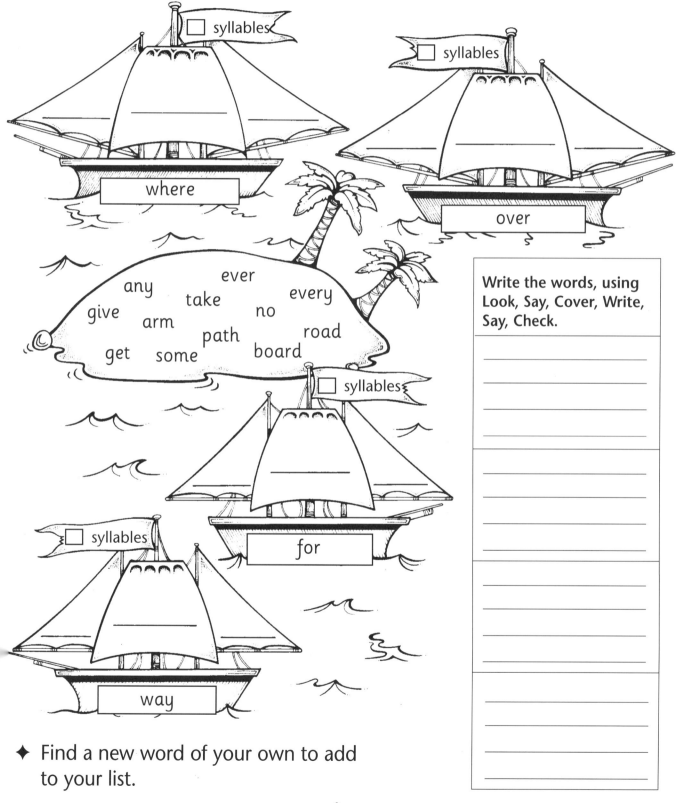

☐ syllables

where

☐ syllables

over

ever
any   take   every
give   arm   no
get   some   path   road
board

☐ syllables

for

☐ syllables

way

Write the words, using Look, Say, Cover, Write, Say, Check.

✦ Find a new word of your own to add to your list.

Common phonemes, different spellings

 Overall aims

- To collect and collate words with common phonemes and different spellings (homophones).
- To identify and recognise middle phonemes.
- To collect and classify words with common spellings but different pronunciations.
- To read and spell words with common spellings but different pronunciations.

 Teacher information

The most important issue concerning all these activities is that children should sound out the words and hear the sounds they are making, but be aware that similar letters may produce different sounds in a written form.
- A phoneme is the smallest unit of sound in a word – cat has three phonemes: c, a, t.
- A grapheme is a letter.
- Many words sound alike but are spelled differently, such as *paw, pour, poor*. These are called homophones from the Greek *homo* meaning the same and *phone* meaning sound. This is a difficult area. Twenty-six letters of the alphabet make up more than 44 sounds in spoken English. This means that children may be following patterns that you have taught them but will still be spelling words incorrectly in context. Try and make homophones fun.

 Intended learning

- To distinguish between rhymes and homophones.
- To collect words and explore sounds.

 Starting point

- From a shared traditional rhyme, such as *One, two, buckle my shoe*, ask children to identify the words that rhyme. They could circle them or appoint a scribe to write them separately on a piece of paper.

Ask them to read and sound out the words carefully. They are rhymes but they are not spelled in the same way, such as *four* and *door*. What letters make the same sounds? Explain that there are groups of words called homophones and give them a definition. Give them some more examples – *bear/bare, be/bee, tale/tail* and discuss meanings. Ask them to find some more examples. Finish the session with another rhyme and ask them to do much of the same work themselves, so you can monitor the level of their knowledge and awareness.

 Group activities

- Give one group a list of words. They have to find out homophones and the meanings of the words.
- Others could use a list as rhymes in fun poems. They should add new words to the class Word Wall, to encourage reading around the classroom.
- What fun stories can children write about a *bare bear*; a *pale pail*; the *tale* of a *tail*; why did the *flea flee*? Encourage them to find more fun pairs.
- Make simple books containing two different words making the same sound on every page, such as *steal/steel, meet/meat, pain/pane*. The children should find the meanings of these words and write them in a meaningful sentence.
- Children at a more advanced stage could make a homophone dictionary to add to the class library.

 Plenary session

Bring the class together again to share ideas. They should list all the homophones they have discovered in the course of the session. Ask them to arrange them in alphabetical order so the list can be used as a spell checker when they are writing. They could isolate the sounds in the words and try to reach some conclusions, such as: Does air always make the same sound? What other letters make this sound? Categorise these in a chart and keep them on the wall for children to consult. They could share the books they have made and explain what they have found out about the sounds of words?

◆LESSON TWO◆

◆ Intended learning

◆ To to collect and collate words with common phonemes, different spellings.
◆ To identify and recognise middle phonemes.
◆ To generate and spell new words.

◆ Starting point

◆ Revise the work from previous lesson, using the same rhymes if necessary. Summarise what the children have learned so far about homophones. To illustrate the principle, you could use jokes from children's joke books that rely on word play through homophones, such as: 'Can I whisper? Sorry, it's not allowed (aloud)!'; 'What did Goldilocks sit on? Bear chairs.'

◆ Using the differentiated activity sheets

Activity sheet 1

This is aimed at children who need to sound out words and classify them according to sound.

Activity sheet 2

This is aimed at those children who can read and recognise words which contain the same middle letters but not necessarily the same phoneme.

Activity sheet 3

This is aimed at a higher level, where children are generating often different sounding words using the letter patterns given and the alphabets on the page.

◆ Plenary session

Bring the class together to discuss their work. Ask some children to write their homophones on the board/Word Wall and to circle the different letters that make the same sound. They should be able to justify their classification strategy. Others could add newly generated words to the word wall and explain which ones make the same sounds and which do not. Children could be prompted: "How can you find out what words are 'correct'? What words are 'nonsense'? Where would you look to find out?" Some children could challenge others to spell the words only given the verbal prompt and a definition, for example "You sunbathe on this next to the sea (beach). This is a tree often with copper-coloured leaves (beech)."

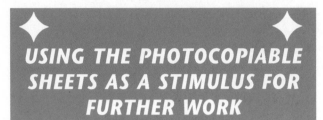

USING THE PHOTOCOPIABLE SHEETS AS A STIMULUS FOR FURTHER WORK

 Activity sheet 1

To consolidate work on words that sound the same, children could:
✦ use the words on the sheet as cards and play snap games or collect families of rhymes;
✦ use the homophones to complete a rhyming couplet. Can children think of more words that make the same sound? Are they spelled differently or the same?;
✦ present one word from the sheet and use the onset and rime technique to generate new words – *flew, stew, new*. Others will soon appear – *flu, phew*.

 Activity sheet 2

To consolidate and extend work on more complicated middle phonemes, children could:
✦ isolate rhymes in sounds and generate more rhymes by analogy, nonsensical or not;
✦ use the examples for odd-one-out games by adding more words that use the same letter patterns;
✦ use the words as headers and build lists under them one at a time.

 Activity sheet 3

To extend work on generating and categorising new words, children could:
✦ make dictionaries, writing one sound for each page and illustrating it with a drawing and a sentence. This links with alphabet skills;
✦ colour the same letters in the lists of words and see what they notice in the patterns. Some children may like to colour suffixes or prefixes only, if they are considering word-building;
✦ cut out the blocks of words and challenge others to identify the common letters.

OTHER IDEAS FOR COMMON PHONEMES WITH DIFFERENT SPELLINGS

✦ Make word wheels and word slides which give the children an opportunity to experiment with sounds and to generate sounds which may have different spellings.

✦ Write poetry and continue with rhyming work. Children can write out and display any books or poems.

✦ Blank out the rhyming words in poems and ask children to provide them anew. Compare their versions with the original. What differences are there in effect and in meaning?

✦ Make up quizzes that link with dictionary work – It buzzes and makes honey. It's the length of time a King or Queen is on the throne.

✦ Write joke books, using jokes from homophonic word play. 'What happens when you blow on a wind instrument? You toot on a flute.'

✦ Write stories, isolating words that are homophones. They could draw small pictures in the place of the words and challenge others to spell the correct word, such as a *bee*, a *tail*.

✦ Research words that are spelled the same but mean different things, such as *saw*. Use this as an opportunity to learn spellings of words such as *two/too/to* and *there/their* – all commonly misspelled.

✦ Who can find out how many different combinations of letters make the same sound? Are there any rules to be formulated?

◆ Common phonemes ◆

◆ Say the name of each picture and write it inside the picture. Then choose the words from the boxes below that have the same sounds but different spellings and write them in the pictures.

sh(oe)   t(wo)   p(aw)   (Ear)th

two	pour	fern	to
poor	burn	flew	dirt
saw	worth	through	store

◆ Now circle the letters in the words that make the same sounds.

✦ Common phonemes ✦

✦ Look at these three words. They all have the same middle letters but make different sounds.

| w (oo) d | f (oo) d | p (oo) r |

✦ Read these words. Circle the letters that are the same in each row. Write more words with the same middle letters. What sounds do they make?

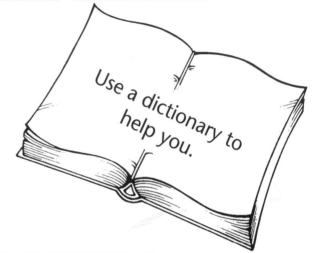

Use a dictionary to help you.

know	bowl	now	_____
marry	part	share	_____
hour	could	four	_____
through	cough	plough	_____
chief	quiet	friend	_____

abcdefghijklmnopqrstuvwxyz

◆ Common phonemes ◆

◆ How many words can you make that use the same letter patterns but make different sounds?

Say the word ◆   Write the word   ◆   Learn the word

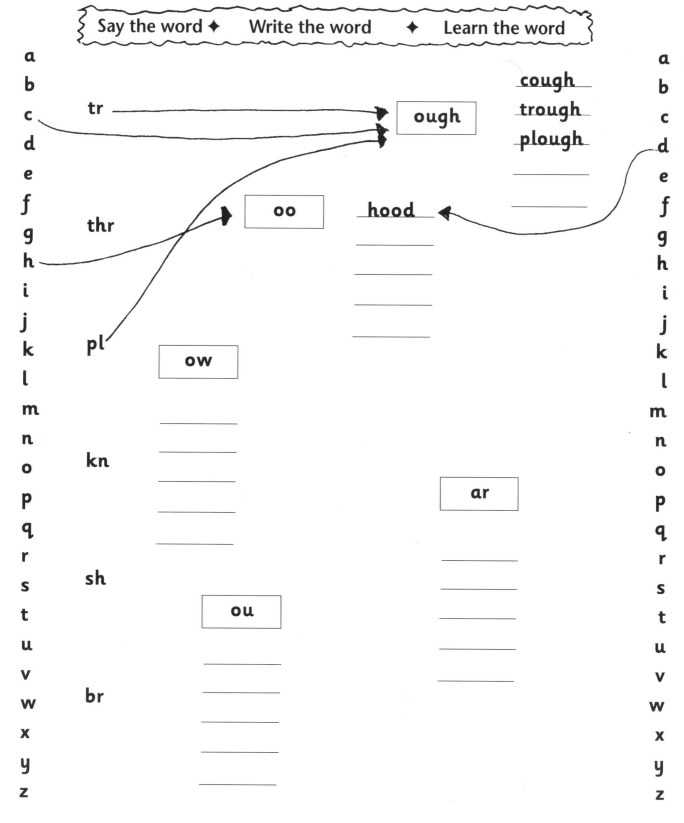

a
b
c tr
d
e
f
g thr
h
i
j
k pl
l
m
n
o kn
p
q
r
s sh
t
u
v
w br
x
y
z

ough

oo

ow

ou

cough
trough
plough
_____
_____

hood
_____
_____
_____
_____

ar
_____
_____
_____
_____
_____

a
b
c
d
e
f
g
h
i
j
k
l
m
n
o
p
q
r
s
t
u
v
w
x
y
z

Spelling
KS2: Y3–4/P4–5

Developing
Literacy
Skills

Photocopiable

45

Spelling verbs

 ### Overall aims

+ To spell regular verb endings.
+ To explore and formulate the common spelling rules.
+ To recognise and learn irregular spellings of tense changes.

 ### Teacher information

The children will need to understand the metalanguage used in this section. You may want to check and revise the use of the terms 'verb' and 'consonant', and ensure that children are familiar with the common verb suffixes *ing* and *ed.* Before the work, you will also need to draw attention to previous knowledge and experience of regular verb roots which do not change at all when the tense is changed, such as *play, played, playing.* As with all rules, there are always exceptions. In general, however, the following rules apply to spelling verbs and their endings:

+ change *y* to *ie* when adding *s;*
+ double the final consonant when adding *ed* and *ing;*
+ drop the *e* when adding *ing.*

The most important issue concerning all these activities is that children should sound out the words and hear the sound they are making.

 **◆ LESSON ONE ◆**

 ### Intended learning

+ To spell regular verb endings.
+ To explore and formulate the common spelling rules.

 ### Starting point

+ Begin by establishing that the lesson will be to explore verbs and their endings, or suffixes. Refer to class word banks of regular verbs and remind

the children of verbs they know, such as *play,* and their endings – *played, playing.* In shared reading, use a laminated text that included examples of regular verbs that use different endings, such as *cry, cried, make, making.* Display them. Begin to explore and identify the changes, and make predictions about new words based on the evidence collected.

 ### Group activities

These activities will focus the children's attention on the spelling rules for verb endings. Provide cards containing the same root verbs for each group so that comparisons can be made in the Plenary session. Let them use dictionaries, word banks and spellcheckers on computers to check the spellings. They should begin to categorise and group the spellings and explain what is happening, then list and display their findings.

+ One group should explore the spelling of these root words when an *s* is added.
+ Another group should explore the spelling of these root words when *ing* is added.
+ Another group should explore the spelling of these words when *ed* is added.

 ### Plenary session

The children should report back on their findings. Begin to formulate and agree on the rules for regular verb endings. Write these headings on four large sheets of paper:

'no change',' double the consonant', '*y* to *ies*' and 'cross off the *e* when adding *ing*'

Take each of the given regular verbs and ask the children to write the word on the correct sheet. Some words will appear on two of the sheets. Use the sheets as a wall display and encourage the children to add to it over time.

◆ Intended learning

✦ To recognise and learn irregular spellings of tense changes.

◆ Starting point

✦ Revise the work from the previous lesson, reminding the children what they discovered about regular verb endings and the rules they discovered. Explain that not all verbs follow the same rules! Some verbs change completely, such as *go, went*. Others change their middle vowel sound, for example *come, came, take, took*.

◆ Using the differentiated activity sheets

Explain to the children that they are going to explore verb endings for themselves. Some will change and others won't. Emphasise that they will be looking for comparisons and applying rules, as well as identifying words that are exceptions to these.

Activity sheet 1

This is aimed at children who will need to further explore the regular verbs, but introducing and recording a few of the exceptions.

Activity sheet 2

This is aimed at children who can begin to recognise and identify irregular verb changes, collecting the words and learning the spelling.

Activity sheet 3

This is aimed at children who can recognise and identify irregular verb changes, and encourages them to collect, spell and categorise the words, using the rules identified to generate by analogy.

◆ Plenary session

After the children have completed their tasks, bring the class together to share and discuss the work. This time can be used to assess understanding, by prompting questions using the words the children have explored.

For Activity sheet 1
Write a regular verb on the board and ask, "Can you read this word to me? Now can you write it with *ing*. What did you change? Why did you do that?" Repeat the activity to check other verb endings.

For Activity sheet 2
Write a word string on the board, using the past tense of the verbs. Take a verb and ask, "Can you find me a word in the string that is the past tense of this verb? What do you notice about the word? Can you write it for me?"

For Activity sheet 3
Write two words that follow the same pattern in the past tense, such as *blew, threw*. Give the child a verb, such as *grow*, and ask them to generate the past tense by analogy.

As a closing activity play *Find my Partner*. Give out pairs of words on cards, and ask the children to find their partner. Have a variety of regular and irregular pairings, such as *play, played, go, went*. Then extend this by asking the children to group themselves according to pattern – *swing, swung, sing, sung, begin, begun* can make a group.

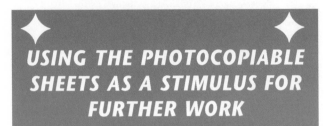

USING THE PHOTOCOPIABLE SHEETS AS A STIMULUS FOR FURTHER WORK

✦ Activity sheet 1

To consolidate their work on regular verb endings, the children could:
✦ play *Happy Families*. Mount a set of verbs in various tenses; the children collect a set and categorise the words;
✦ play *What's the Rule Bingo*. Provide verb base-boards and a matching number of individual cards highlighting the particular rules. The children take turns to pick a card and cover a word on their baseboard with the correct rule, for example the child picks up a card saying 'double the consonant when adding *ing*'. This is placed over the word *stop* on the baseboard.

✦ Activity sheet 2

To consolidate their work on past tense vowels, the children could:
✦ create word strings for a friend to unscramble;
✦ write their own cloze procedure stories and share them with others, asking for suggestions for appropriate verbs and the correct tense ending.

✦ Activity sheet 3

To consolidate their work on looking for patterns and generating by analogy, the children could:
✦ create a word search for a friend to try;
✦ collect verbs that change the vowel sound in the past tense. Generate their own spelling by analogy and use word banks and dictionaries to check the accuracy of their attempts.
✦ in guided reading sessions and in their own reading, collect examples of the past tense. Record and categorise according to the rules identified by the class and note any words which do not seem to belong to any category!

OTHER IDEAS FOR SPELLING VERBS

✦ Compare and contrast rules for nouns and verbs, such as *y* changing to an *i* when adding suffixes, as in *marry* to *married* and *happy* to *happily*.

✦ Be alert to colloquial and dialectical variations in forming the past tense, or errors that occur when the child is a user of English as an additional language. Provide opportunities to reinforce the standard form. It is worth exploring the rules the children themselves have established, through exploring words in text, to highlight and reinforce the correct usage in a non-threatening way.

Generally, encourage the children to use the **Look, Say, Cover, Write, Say, Check** method for learning spellings.

Keep in mind that there is a real relationship between handwriting and spelling. Writing letter strings in a consistent and regular way helps children to register patterns in a multi-sensory way.

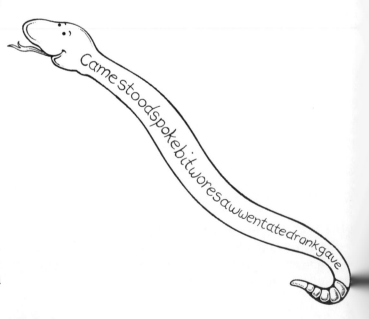

◆ Stepping stones ◆

◆ Write the correct letter in each stepping stone to change the ending for each root word.

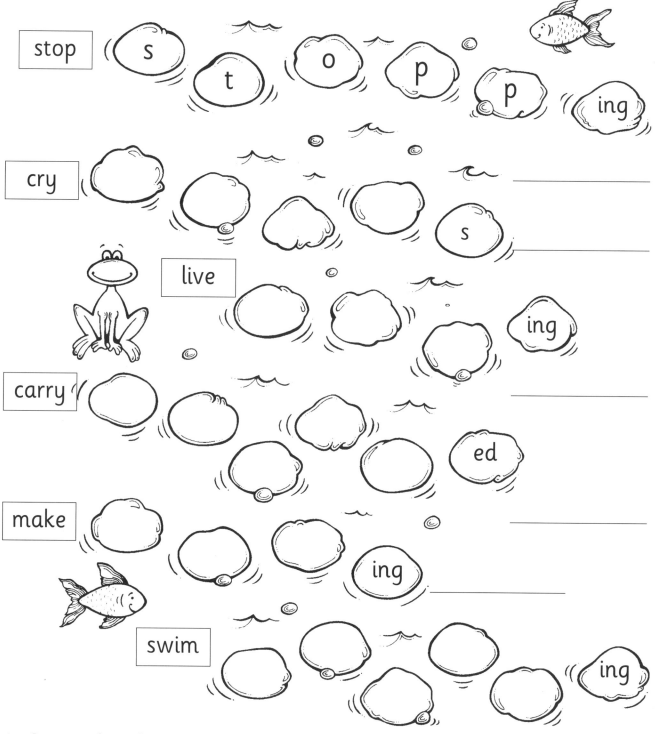

stop   s   t   o   p   p   ing

cry   s _____

live   ing _____

carry   ed _____

make   ing _____

swim   ing _____

◆ On another sheet of paper, write each word in a sentence.

✦ Word snakes ✦

✦ The past tenses of the verbs below are hidden in the word snake. Find them and write them under their partners.

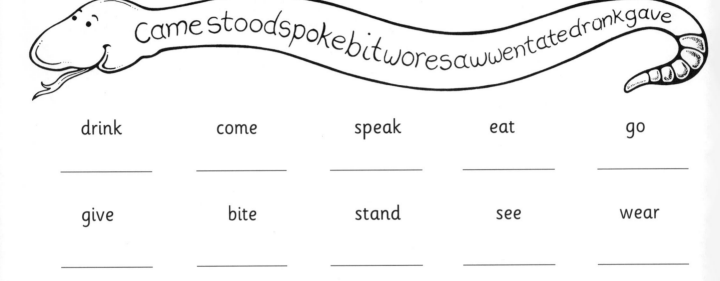

Camestoodspokebitworesawwentatedrankgave

drink	come	speak	eat	go
_____	_____	_____	_____	_____

give	bite	stand	see	wear
_____	_____	_____	_____	_____

✦ Here are some more past tenses but they are jumbled up! Sort them out and match them to their partners.

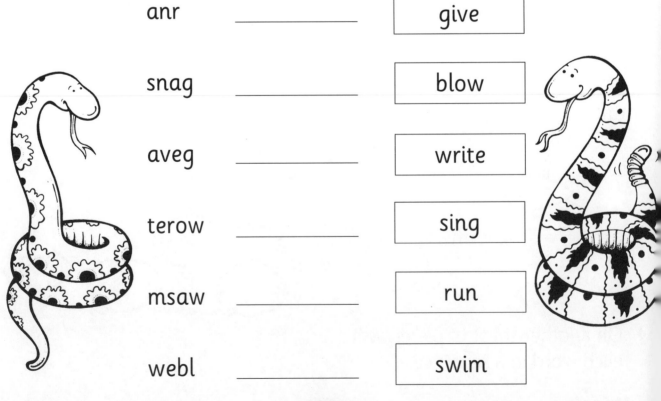

anr	_____	give
snag	_____	blow
aveg	_____	write
terow	_____	sing
msaw	_____	run
webl	_____	swim

Developing
literacy
Skills

◆ Changing tense ◆

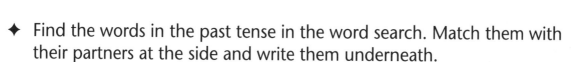

◆ Find the words in the past tense in the word search. Match them with their partners at the side and write them underneath.

fall								sit
_____								_____
blow	d	b	t	r	a	n		know
_____	r	l	f	e	l	l		_____
go	a	e	o	x	v	s		sing
_____	n	w	w	s	a	w		_____
swim	k	n	e	w	y	a		drink
_____	s	a	n	g	f	m		_____
see	s	a	t	v	j	p		run
_____								_____

◆ What do you notice about the words? Can you spot a pattern?

_____

_____

◆ Do any words not fit with your pattern? Why not?

_____   because   _____

_____   _____

◆ Use the words you have found to help you write the past tense of these verbs.

throw _____   begin _____   swing _____

sink _____   grow _____

Developing
literacy
Skills

Inflectional endings

 Overall aims

✦ To investigate and collect words with common inflectional endings.
✦ To spell and read words with common inflectional endings.
✦ To generate and learn new words with common inflectional endings.

 Teacher information

Children should sound out words and sounds they are making, but realise that the same sounds are not always represented by the same letter patterns. Words with endings such as *tion*, *ial* and *ious* are notoriously difficult to spell, as they make sounds unlike those normally associated with the letters. Children should be taught to recognise these endings through print. They can learn to write them by recognising and practising patterns and shapes. Help them to grasp the concept of stressed syllables, such as "Is the *tion* in 'attention' the stressed syllable?" Work on homophones is also important for spelling difficult word endings.

 **LESSON ONE**

 Intended learning

✦ To revise the idea of similar sounds not being represented by similar letter patterns.
✦ To recognize and investigate words with common inflectional endings.
✦ To read words with common inflectional endings and attempt to interpret patterns of spelling.

 Starting point

✦ Start with a simple and silly rhyme:

Said the flea to the bee,
It's a mystery to me
How, with wings that are wee,
You can fly so easily.

Ask someone to read the verse and point to the words that rhyme. Circle the word endings that make the sound and note that they all have the same ending sound, but each is spelled differently. Look at words like addition and subtraction and identify the final sounds (*shun*). The fact that no words in English end with *shun* should be noted. However, other words using the *ion* ending, such as television and division follow a different pattern. Categorise these words on the board under their endings. Chant some of them together to break them down into syllables. Which syllables sound silly if they are stressed? They should find that the syllable before the ending sound is stressed.

 Group activities

✦ Using dictionaries, each group takes a different sound: *tion*, *ious*, *ial* and finds words with these endings, writing them in a sentence, some with the correct spelling and at least one using *shun*, *shus*, *shall* instead. They can test out other members of the class later. You could make it a competition by giving a set period of time.
✦ The group that will find these difficult should be given a more simple ending, such as *ight* from which they can rhyme by analogy.

They should all stress the syllables in the words and find which is stressed when the word is spoken.

 Plenary session

Let the groups test each other with their trick sentences. How do they know which are correct? What have they learned about the endings using these sounds that can help them? Share the *ight* words. Do any end in *ite*?

When they spoke the words to emphasise the stresses, did they all have stressed syllables before the ending? Is this a pattern?

Outline some of the strange endings and their sounds again.

Keep the words displayed for the next session.

Inflectional endings

 Intended learning

- To investigate and collect words with common inflectional endings.
- To spell and read words with common inflectional endings using shape as a clue.
- To generate and learn new words with common inflectional endings.

 Starting point

- Revise the work of the previous lesson by saying: "Sit to attention. Do you want to do some addition, subtraction or division?" Ask them why you used these words. Write up some of the words, including difficult ones, from each group – *competition, ferocious, special.*
- Ask children to come up, circle the endings and sound them out. Now ask them to draw boxes around all the letters in the words. Rub out the letters. What shapes are left? Are they all different?
- If you told them the word again, or gave them the first few letters, could they write it in the boxes? Stress that these words are difficult and that their first attempt may not always be correct. How could they find the correct spellings of the word?

Using the differentiated activity sheets

Activity sheet 1

This has been designed for children who need to read and identify common inflectional endings in words. It also asks them to categorise these words according to sound.

Activity sheet 2

This helps children recognise difficult word endings by their shape, thus reinforcing visual awareness.

Activity sheet 3

This is more difficult, in that it asks children to generate words using given endings and also to check their spelling.

 Plenary session

Bring the class together and ask each group to explain what they have done.

- One group should explain what words they put into particular sound categories and justify their choices. Words should be written on a Word Wall under these sound categories. Can others in the class think of any more words to write in the boxes?
- Another group could explain the concept of shape boxes and test them out on other children. What rules can be devised from this method, for example *tion* and *ial* always have the same shape; *ious* could be trickier as it has no distinctive ascender.
- What other inflectional endings can children recognise that do not fall into these patterns, such as *ough*, *ight*? What shapes do they make?
- Finally, discuss how necessary it is to try out their spellings and not be concerned that they are correct first time. What can they use to help them find the correct spelling?
- Look at all the new words on the Word Wall and ask children to read the words, spell out the final letters and make the sound.

Inflectional endings

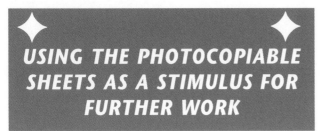

USING THE PHOTOCOPIABLE SHEETS AS A STIMULUS FOR FURTHER WORK

Activity sheet 1

+ Produce simple cloze exercises. The children blank out word endings and ask partners to complete the word appropriately.
+ They say a word on the sheet and ask partners to tell them what other words are on the sheet containing the same word ending. Pointing at them would also be useful.
+ They read some words on the sheet and reinforce the end sound – *question/shun*. They should then point to and read another word on the sheet using that ending, such as *fraction*.

Activity sheet 2

+ Children could draw shapes of the end sounds only as their partners say a word.
+ They present the shape only and ask questions, such as "Is this word *action*?" They have to give reasons for their answer, such as "It is not long enough. It does not have a tall box four letters from the end."
+ Some could blank out some letters in the completed shape boxes and ask partners to finish the spelling of the words.

Activity sheet 3

+ Let children cut out the boxes, hand them out and ask which are the correct spellings.
+ Some could ask others to check the words again in a dictionary.
+ Blank out the first word-ending column and ask children what these endings should be from reading the examples.

OTHER IDEAS FOR INFLECTIONAL ENDINGS

+ Use collections of words to develop work on parts of speech. *Creation* is a noun, what is the verb? *Television* is a noun, what is the verb? Give the children lists and challenge them to change them into these different parts of speech.

+ Make 'transformation books' to show how parts of speech can be transformed from one to another – nouns are objects, people or places, and verbs are to do with action or being. For example, 'I did some addition. The teacher told us how to add.'

+ Work on stress in sentences and how stressing the wrong word can change meaning – 'He was *walking* down the road' is different in emphasis from '*He* was walking down the road.' Say what the differences are. Children could make up other examples to test their friends.

+ Breaking down words into their constituent parts involves looking at the roots of words. This can often help us to learn to spell words, for example *compete* (with an *e*) is the root of *competition*.

+ Experiment with a talking word processor to see how sounds in words can be influenced by adding or removing letters – *it, in, ion, ious, tin, tion*.

+ Ask children to break down long complicated words into smaller building blocks. This can be done through syllable practice but also by using the idea of word maths, such as:
population – ion + e = populate.
Children can challenge each other orally as well as using pen and paper.

Developing literacy Skills

✦ Investigate endings ✦

✦ Write the words in the correct boxes.

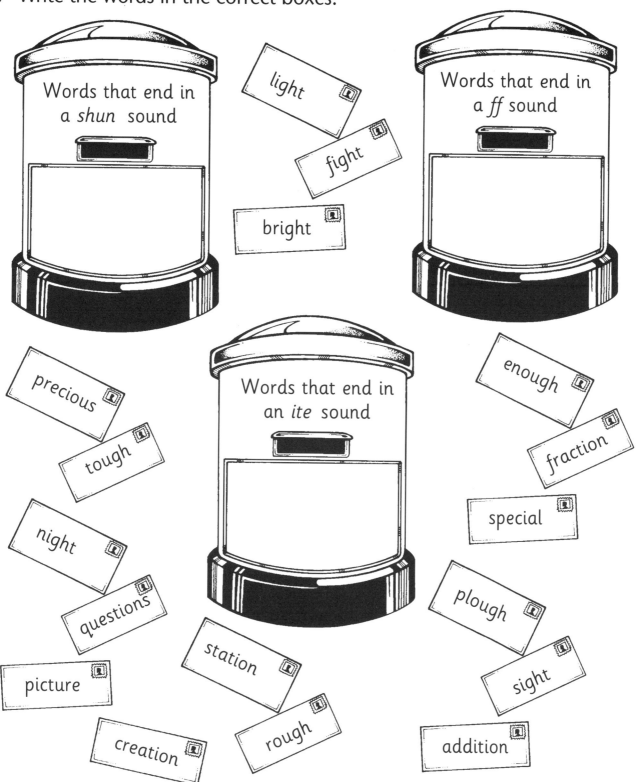

✦ Now write more examples in each box.

Name _____

◆ Shapes ◆

✦ Write each word in its correct shape. Write the words in the box at the bottom of the page.

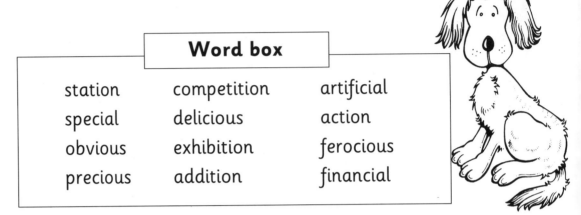

Word box

station	competition	artificial
special	delicious	action
obvious	exhibition	ferocious
precious	addition	financial

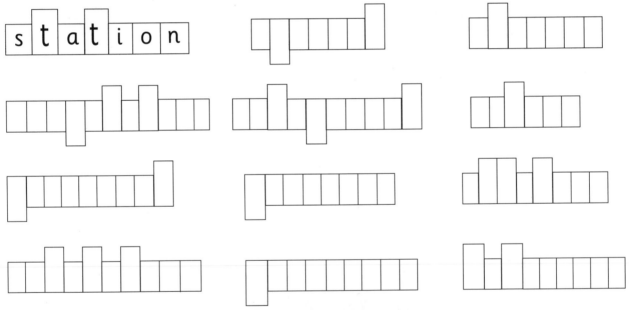

s t a t i o n

station

Developing Literacy Skills

Photocopiable

◆ Check your spelling ◆

◆ Complete the chart with as many examples as you can find.
Use your dictionary to check your spelling.

Word ending	New words My first attempt	Checked in a dictionary. It spells like this.	Right first time	Right second time
– ion	atension	attention		✔
– ough				
– ight				
– ial				
– ious			Score box	Score box

Dictionaries and thesauruses

Overall aims

◆ To use dictionaries, word banks and spelling logs to investigate and check spelling.
◆ To identify misspelled words in own writing, collect, practise and learn to spell them.
◆ To use personal word banks as a basis for investigating other words with similar patterns and meanings.
◆ To use the thesaurus, dictionaries and other reading to explore synonyms and homonyms, linked to work on word puzzles.

Teacher information

Children should be aware of the words they can spell and have ownership of a spelling repertoire. Building up spelling logs and word banks enables them to reflect on their growth as spellers. They will experience, through their work, the terminology appropriate to the task, and will develop knowledge and understanding of categories, word-ordering and sequencing. Awareness of the words or rules they find problematic can help children to avoid spelling pitfalls, and can be of great support to the less confident speller. Collections of tricky words can provide an invaluable resource.

LESSON ONE

Intended learning

◆ To use dictionaries, word banks and spelling logs to investigate and check spelling
◆ To identify misspelled words in own writing, collect, practise and learn to spell them.

Starting point

◆ Use an enlarged example of a first draft of written work. This should be a child's although this would need sensitive handling. Maybe an older child in the school would volunteer a piece. There will need to be enough errors to work on but not too many as to make the task unmanageable. Read it to the class. Ask them to identify the spelling errors. List them on the board and see how many they can correct using their acquired knowledge of spelling rules and referring to class collections. Demonstrate how to use a dictionary to see if they were right and to look up unknown words. Remind them about alphabetical order and refer to alphabet charts and friezes.

Group activities

◆ Give the groups other examples of first drafts to check for spelling errors. List them and identify what corrections need to be made, according to known spelling rules.
◆ The children write and record 'I know these words'. First, brainstorm the words they can write, generating the list by analogy. For more confident, prolific spellers it may be best to set a time limit. Using alphabet charts and dictionaries, they sort and list their words in alphabetical order.
◆ In a guided writing activity, they can explore drafts of their own work. List errors and explore common error patterns. Record these as a collection: 'My Tricky Words'. Use **Look, Say, Cover, Write, Say, Check** to learn the spellings. This activity can be returned to on a regular basis. Children can check their list, identifying and removing words that are no longer tricky for them and recording any new ones they have found.

Plenary session

Each group reports back on the activities and puts the work on a working wall display. As a closing activity choose a category, or a topic such as 'plants', and ask for contributions – 'Words about plants that we can spell'. Display the words in a class word bank. Revise and add to this regularly, and encourage the children to do so, first checking that their spelling is accurate.

◆LESSON TWO◆

◆ Intended learning

◆ To use personal word banks as a basis for investigating other words with similar patterns and meanings.

◆ Starting point

◆ Revise the work from the previous lesson, reminding the children what they discovered about identifying, correcting and organising spellings. Refer them to the class word banks and explain that the following activities will help them to build up their own spelling collections.

◆ Using the differentiated activity sheets

Activity sheet 1

This is aimed at children who are experiencing difficulty with spelling and need to explore alphabetical order so that they can access dictionaries as a spelling source more easily.

Activity sheet 2

This is aimed at children who have progressed as spellers, but need further experience of dictionaries to assist them in developing self-correcting strategies.

Activity sheet 3

This is aimed at children who can classify and sort words, are confident in using dictionaries and are ready to extend their vocabulary knowledge.

◆ Plenary session

After the children have completed their tasks, bring the whole class together to share and discuss the work. This time can also be used to assess the understanding of each group, by prompting questions using word collections and dictionaries.

For Activity sheet 1
Provide a variety of words on a magnetic board, such as *apple, pear, banana, orange*. Ask someone to arrange the words in alphabetical order. Then ask the child to name the category – 'fruit' – and add another word to the list. For a further activity, the child could generate another group of words and take the role of teacher to guide another member of the class.

For Activity sheet 2
Write two words on the board, such as *takeing/ taking*. Ask a child to identify which is the correct spelling and explain why, erasing the spelling mistake. Ask the child to generate another word that follows the same rule.

For Activity sheet 3
One child writes one of the words from the activity sheet, reading it aloud. Ask "What does the word mean? Tell me another word that goes with it." For example, the child may have chosen *sapphire*, and could provide another jewel, or may have selected other *ph* words such as *phonic*.

As a closing activity, ask each child in turn to write a word relating to a given category, such as 'animals', or a given pattern, such as *ight*. Be sensitive to the less confident spellers, providing easier words or prompts if required.

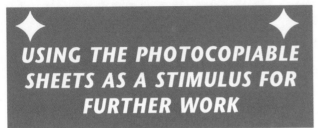

Dictionaries and thesauruses

USING THE PHOTOCOPIABLE SHEETS AS A STIMULUS FOR FURTHER WORK

Activity sheet 1

+ Produce a class dictionary for the different work areas in the class – 'Words we need in the maths corner'. Explore the words on a computer spellchecker. Edit and arrange them, using fonts and graphics related to the area. Display them.
+ Design, make and play a *Happy Families* or *Bingo* game for the categories, ensuring that the spelling is accurate.
+ Explore errors in their own work, using the options provided on a spellchecker. For example, "I wrote *swiming*. The spellchecker said *swimming*, so I must have forgotten to double the consonant when I added *ing*."

Activity sheet 2

+ Introduce proofreading. Explore ways of marking the text. Discussing the most effective ways.
+ Explore a 'Tricky Words' collection. Develop mnemonics or word play strategies to help memorise them.
+ Investigate the options on spellcheckers for a spelling error. (On one computer the mistake *shoping* generated 10 different possibilities, all verbs, all ending in *ing*.)

Activity sheet 3

+ Identify unknown words during reading. Find out what they mean and list, group and learn them.
+ Use a thesaurus to explore sets of words. Think about how these could be recorded – words for angry could be listed in order of severity, from miffed to cross to furious!
+ Investigate analogies – *wool/sheep, fur/rabbit, feathers/?* Play *Pairs*. Collect examples and devise puzzles and games for other groups to play.

OTHER IDEAS FOR DICTIONARIES AND THESAURUSES

David Crystal in his book *The Cambridge Encyclopedia of Language*, defines synonyms and homonyms as follows:

Synonyms – words that have the same meaning as another word.

Homonyms – words which have the same form but different meanings.

Synonyms

+ Play *Pairs*. The children have to match the words which have the same meaning, such as: *commence/begin, permit/allow, expensive/dear*.
+ Create word searches or crosswords, giving one word and asking the children to find a word that means the same in the puzzle.
+ Use a text to investigate alternative words the author could have used. Discuss which words are most effective in setting the scene or giving an impression, for example is *big* or *gigantic* a better way to describe the mountain?

Homonyms

+ Make silly pictures to illustrate these – the post came through the letter box, a coat of paint, my mouse isn't working – modern usage of old words!

+ Research colloquialisms, such as someone who is afraid is called a 'chicken', while a Londoner in the East End might be said to have 'no bottle', meaning the same thing. Children could collect examples of these and illustrate them literally.

+ Children who use English as an additional language are often confused by homonyms. Draw attention to them to ensure that the meaning has been ascertained in the right context. Explore examples in other languages.

Developing *literacy* Skills

◆ Put us in order! ◆

◆ Use a dictionary to find out how to spell these words.

◆ Write the words you have found in the dictionary in alphabetical order.

◆ Choose six words from your 'Tricky words' list. Write them here in alphabetical order.

◆ Use a thesaurus to find six words that mean the same as *big*. Write them in alphabetical order.

Spelling

S2: Y3–4/P4–5

Developing
Literacy
Skills

Photocopiable

61

◆ Tricky words ◆

Can you help me? I find these words really tricky! Use a dictionary to correct my spelling.

peice

shoping

buble

_____

_____

_____

takeing

wolfs

lite

_____

_____

_____

✦ Write each of the words again in the boxes below. Find three more words for each box to follow the same pattern.

Developing
literacy
Skills

✦ **What does it mean?** ✦

✦ Look at the words
   in each circle.

✦ Use a dictionary to
   find out what each
   word means.

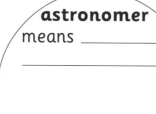

astronomer
means _____
_____

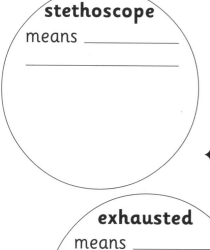

stethoscope
means _____
_____

celebration
means _____
_____

✦ Use a thesaurus to collect
   other words related to the
   first word. Write them in
   the circle.

exhausted
means _____
_____

sapphire
means _____
_____

✦ Use Look, Say, Cover, Write, Say, Check to learn the words.
   Be careful! They are tricky!

Word	Try it	Try again	Last time!
stethoscope			
astronomer			
celebration			
sapphire			
exhausted			

A dreadful language?

I take it you already know
Of tough and bough and cough and dough?
Others may stumble, but not you
On hiccough, thorough, laugh and through.
Well done! And now you wish, perhaps,
To learn of less familiar traps?

Beware of heard, a dreadful word
That looks like beard and sounds like bird.
And dead: it's said like bed, not bead –
For goodness sake, don't call it 'deed'!
Watch out for meat and great and threat,
They rhyme with suite and straight and debt.

A moth is not a moth in mother
Nor both in bother, broth in brother.
And here is not a match for there
Nor dear and fear for bear and pear.
And then there's dose and rose and lose –
Just look them up – and goose and choose.

And cork and word and card and ward,
And font and front and word and sword,
And do and go and thwart and cart –
Come, come I've hardly made a start!
A dreadful language? Man alive,
I'd mastered it when I was five.

Hints for pronunciation for foreigners by T.S.W